The Rainbow
All Different All Equal

By Mattie Yeta

CW01044132

I've made my bed, and I'm ready to go to the park. Can we go now please! Dad said he would take us to the park once I finished making my bed.

"OK, Ted, it's a beautiful sunny morning, so today we are walking to Rainbow Park instead of cycling."

Dad, why is that little boy sitting while being pushed? Should they be going to the park?

Your friend is in a wheelchair because their legs don't work properly. That doesn't mean they can't play in the park too.

"Look, Dad, I can see Sarah and her mom. Why is Sarah always with her mom?"

"Ted, not all families have a mom and a dad. However, sometimes, families have a dad who can also be a mom. And in this case, your friend Sarah has a mom who is also a dad.

"People all around the world have many different physical features and personality traits, son. Sometimes, we pick out the differences a lot easier, and sometimes, we don't. Molly's may not be as easy to pick out, but I bet she's working hard along with her family to do the best she can to play with you."

Printed in Great Britain
by Amazon

67485621R00020